ERNEST BLOCH

SUITE MODALE
FOR
FLUTE AND PIANO

BROUDE BROTHERS LIMITED

New York

Suite Modale may also be performed in a version for flute solo and string orchestra, prepared in 1959 by the composer.

The full score to the flute-and-string version has been published in two sizes: in large format (25.5 cm. x 33 cm.), and, in Broude Brothers' Contemporary Composers Study Score Series (No. BB 10), in study score format (19.5 cm. x 25.7 cm.). These scores are available for purchase. String parts for the flute-and-string version are also available for sale.

The flute parts for the flute/piano and the flute/string orchestra versions are identical.

To Elaine Shaffer
Suite Modale
For Flute and Piano

Duration: **12** minutes

ERNEST BLOCH
(1956)

I

Broude Brothers Limited
New York & Williamstown
Printed in U.S.A.

B. B. **2010**

II

III

ERNEST BLOCH

SUITE MODALE

FOR

FLUTE AND PIANO

FLUTE

BROUDE BROTHERS LIMITED
New York

The flute solo on the following pages may be used for both the flute-and-piano and the flute-and-strings versions of *Suite Modale*.

Suite Modale

For Flute and Piano

Duration: **12** minutes

FLUTE

ERNEST BLOCH
(1956)

I

B. B. **2010**

Broude Brothers Limited
New York & Williamstown
Printed in U.S.A.

II

III

Allegro giocoso (♩.= 92)

IV

IV